BRAIN GAMES

First published in the UK in 2023 by Studio Press,
an imprint of Bonnier Books UK,
4th Floor, Victoria House, Bloomsbury Square, London WC1B 4DA
Owned by Bonnier Books,
Sveavägen 56, Stockholm, Sweden

www.bonnierbooks.co.uk

1 3 5 7 9 10 8 6 4 2

All rights reserved
ISBN 978-1-80078-567-0

Written by Roland Hall
Edited by Jackie McCann
Designed by Maddox Philpot & Rob Ward
Production by Giulia Caparrelli

MIX
Paper from
responsible sources
FSC® C018072

A CIP catalogue record for this book is available from the British
Library. Printed and bound in Great Britain by Clays Ltd, Elcograf S.p.A.

MARVEL

BRAIN GAMES

FUN PUZZLES
FOR BRIGHT MINDS

STUDIO PRESS

INTRODUCTION

As every super hero knows, it takes brains to solve a problem. Sure, you need a bit of brawn from time to time – take Banner for example – he's much more likely to find a creative solution to a problem than his green alter-ego, The Incredible Hulk (with his tried and tested methods). A great way to exercise your brain and to keep it in fine shape is to practise mental gymnastics. Or in this case, solve puzzles. Using your grey matter to work out a hidden code, to spot a difference, to calculate a sum or to deduct an answer from a series of clues will keep you happy and focused for hours, and it's good for you!

And when those puzzles are themed around your favourite super heroes (and villains) from your favourite comics, that makes it all the more fun! That's where this book comes in. It's filled with puzzles featuring many Marvel characters, from your friendly neighbourhood Spider-Man to Doctor Doom, from Black Panther to Black Widow and from Wanda to Vision (that sounds like a good combo!).

You'll find a variety of puzzle types too, from simple number challenges and spot the difference, to complicated word puzzles and memory tests. There are even a few taxing quizzes to test your knowledge of Marvel's marvellous world of comic-book characters.

When you start a puzzle, remember to read the instructions carefully, because sometimes there are important rules you need to follow that will make the puzzle work properly. And if you find yourself stuck, you can always grab your parents or carers, or friends and family and ask them for help – we are "stronger together" after all. You can even challenge your pals to a timed problem-solving battle!

So sharpen your pencil, take a deep breath and get stuck in to this fun, brain-boosting series of puzzles and challenges.

TURN TO THE BACK OF THE BOOK TO FIND THE ANSWERS. YOU'LL FIND BLANK PAGES THERE, TOO, THAT YOU CAN USE TO WORK OUT THESE BRAIN TWISTERS!

THE PUZZLES

PUZZLE 1
SPEED TEST

Using the clues below, can you work out – in 30 seconds or less – the identities of these four comic characters?

1

Red – Twin brother – Telekinetic

2

Artificial Intelligence – Robot – Hank Pym

3

Radiation – Web – Peter Parker

4

Spy – S.H.I.E.L.D. – Black

To escape from prison, Scott Lang needs to activate his suit and reduce himself to the size of an ant. He still needs to find the way out of the maze though... can you help him plot a path to freedom?

PUZZLE 3
WHO AM I?

One of Black Panther's entourage has gone missing. Can you work out who it is from the letter clues below? We've filled in a few letters to get you started.

Can you work out who it is from the letter clues below?

The right letter in the right place looks like this:

The right letter in the wrong place looks like this:

And if the letter is not in the word it looks like this:

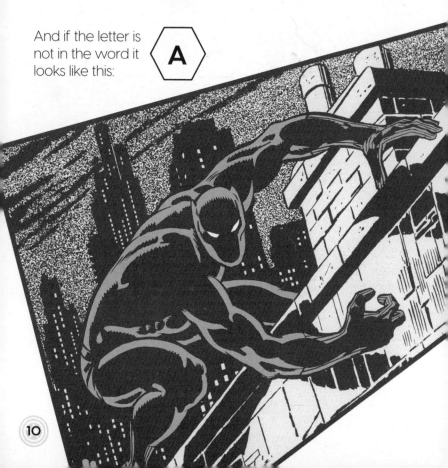

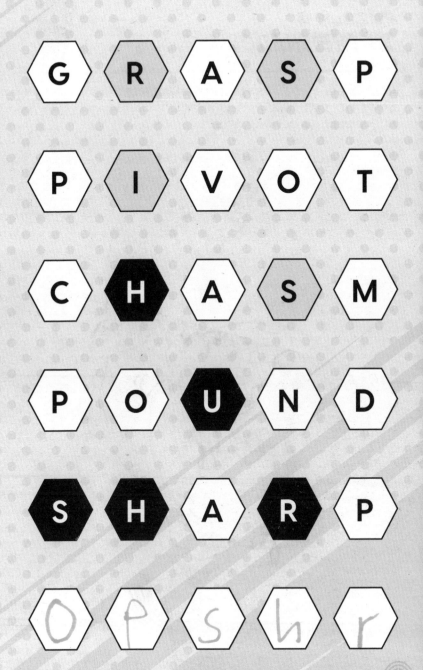

GRASP

PIVOT

CHASM

POUND

SHARP

O P s h r

IN THE SHADOWS

Only one of these shadows is an exact match for Captain America. But which one it is?

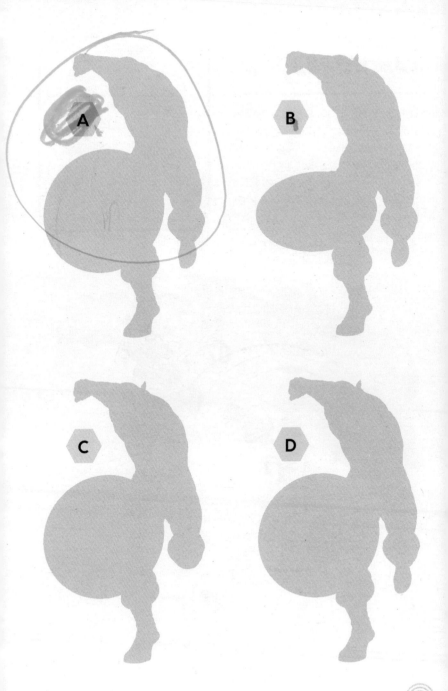

PUZZLE 5
LAB WORK

Bruce Banner is hard at work on a formula in the lab. Can you help him calculate the final formula by filling in all the blanks? The number in each circle must be the sum of the two numbers below.

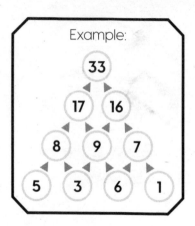

Example:

33
17 16
8 9 7
5 3 6 1

87

....

19 22

....

2 6 ...... 7 ......

Can you pair the word parts below to create the names of five super heroes?

VAL

MAG

CON

SH

GR

KYRIE

NETO

FAL

URI

OOT

PUZZLE 7
WHO'S WHO HEROES?

Many super heroes have an alter ego, an ordinary name which they are known by. Can you match the alter egos on the left to the super heroes on the right?

1   **Bruce Banner**

2   **Steve Rogers**

3   **Tony Stark**

4   **T'Challa**

5   **Doreen Allene Green**

6   **Clint Barton**

7   **Scott Lang**

8   **Natasha Romanoff**

9   **Wanda Maximoff**

10   **Carol Danvers**

11   **Donald Blake**

To make it tougher, we've left an extra name, but which one is it?

A Ant-Man

B Black Panther

C Squirrel Girl

D Captain America

E Captain Marvel

F Hawkeye

G Hulk

H Iron Man

I Black Widow

J Scarlet Witch

PUZZLE 8
IN THE SHADOWS

Black Panther has cast a shadow, but only one of them is an exact match. Can you tell which one?

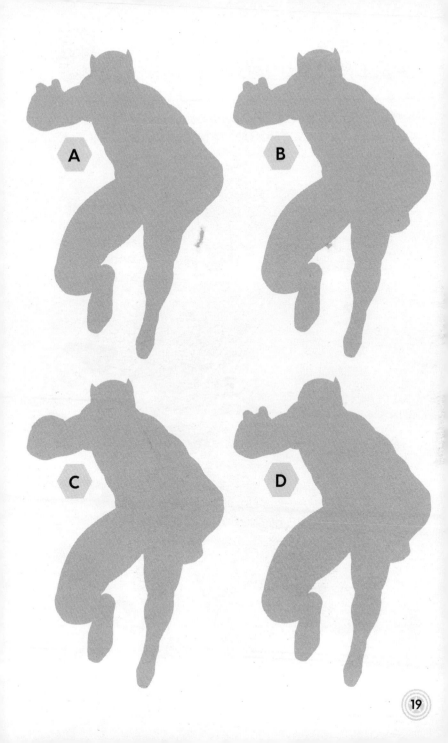

WEIGH-IN

Hulk must balance equal weights across his back. Can you place the six numbers in the blocks so that the totals for each pile are the same?

Clue: you may need to look at the numbers another way up

PUZZLE 10
PLACE A NUMBER

Fill the empty boxes in the grid with the numbers 1, 2, 3, 4 and 5, always following the three rules:

A number must not appear more than once in a row.

A number must not appear more than once in a column.

A number must not appear more than once in each shaded shape.

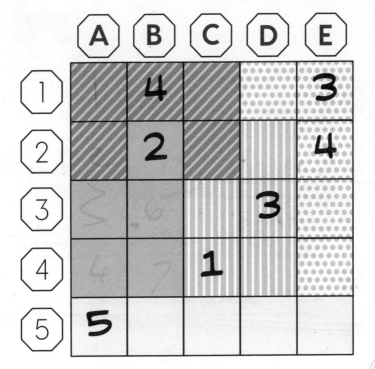

PUZZLE 11
ORDER!

Can you place the five characters in the correct order of first appearance?

- **A** Star-Lord
- **B** Squirrel Girl
- **C** Captain America
- **D** Valkyrie
- **E** The Incredible Hulk

1 Star lord

2 Squirrel Girl

3 captain America

4

5

Can you identify the super hero from the list of other people who have featured in their comics?

1

_____

Monica Rambeau
Genis-Vell
Marie Danvers

2

_____

Rhodey Rhodes
Edwin Jarvis
The Mandarin

3

_____

Tyr
Bor
Odin
Laufey

4

_____

May Parker
John Jonah Jameson Jr.
Harry Lyman

5

_____

Charles Xavier
Magda
Eisenhardt
Wanda Maximoff

PUZZLE 13
PICTURE THIS

Having a memory for everything is a useful tool, as super villain Baron Zemo knows. But are you a match for him? Look at the heads opposite for 30 seconds, then cover them up and take the test!

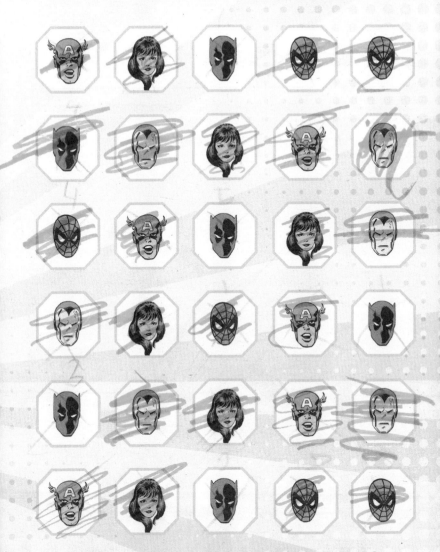

In the space below, write down how many of
each head you saw.

PUZZLE 14
BUZZ WORDSEARCH

Can you help the Wasp find the characters, objects and places in the word panel on the right, hidden in the grid beneath it? They can be read horizontally, vertically or diagonally, and from right to left, or from left to right.

ARROW
BLINK
CLOAK
ERNST
HAMMER
HYPERSPACE
JOSEPH

KORATH
KREE
MANTA
MBAKU
ODIN
PLANET
RONAN THE ACCUSER

SHIELD
STAFF
SUPER HERO
SURTUR
WANDA
WASP
XANDAR

```
B R S R K S M E R U T A S T A
R O I H Y U M K O R A T H R P
O K L S I P A K N H E P M S R
B O B L R E T H A F S O A T T
S T A F F R L T N E R W C H E
J O S E P H F D T P E E G H P
L A Y D D E T A H T S R I K E
M C E W O R R A E T D F N Q C
B A T S T O O S A E U T E S S
A L F H B N U J C N F L M X T
K A I M A R N K C A R G A S K
U X N N T M A G U L D N N J A
C V E U K H M V S P D N I D O
U H R E N K R E E A T N A M L
X E D E C A P S R E P Y H W C
```

Something's up with Iron Man! It's time to focus and see if you can spot five differences between these two images.

PUZZLE 16
MULTIPLE CHOICE

Can you answer the questions correctly in this multiple-choice quiz? The answers are there for you, just pick the right ones!

1

What is the name of Thor's naughty brother?

A. **Loki**

B. **Odin**

C. **Smokey**

D. **Thive**

2

What war did Captain America fight in?

A. **The Boer War**

B. **World War I**

C. **World War II**

D. **The Wakanda War**

3

Which race of aliens had a famous war with the Skrull?

A. **Cotati**

B. **Chitauri**

C. **Kree**

D. **Signori**

4

What is Captain America's shield made of?

A. Captonium

B. Platinum

C. Plutonium

D. Vibranium

5

How many Infinity Stones are there?

A. 3

B. 4

C. 5

D. 6

6

What country does T'Challa rule over?

A. Mexico

B. Namibia

C. Wessex

D. Wakanda

UNDERCOVER

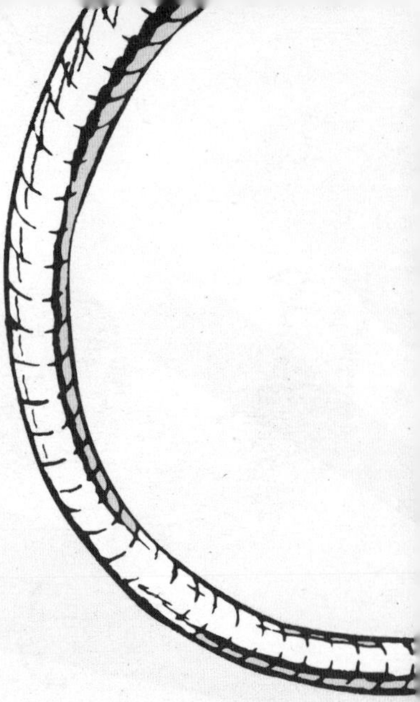

Criminal mastermind Doctor Octopus is in a bit of a tangle. Can you help him work out these curious names?

Clue: they are all anagrams

1
CATARINA MACPIE

2
ANN MIRO

3
ARNOLD CRAVES

4
PETR POPPETS

5
FRETA JONES

7 SAM TIN

6 NANCE RUBBER

8 ERIK ALVY

STARS AND STRIPES

Captain America's shield is based on the flag of the United States of America. But how much do you know about the makeup of the American flag?

Number of red stripes:

_____

Number of white stripes:

_____

Number of stars:

_____

PUZZLE 19
PYRAMID POWER

Tony Stark needs some help testing a new suit in the lab. But first he needs to work out the missing numbers from this pyramid. Can you help? Each number is the sum of the squares below it.

For an extra challenge, do this without writing anything down.

Then attempt the ultra challenge and complete the pyramid in under a minute.

PUZZLE 20
IN THE SHADOWS

Only one of the shadows opposite is an exact match for The Incredible Hulk, but which one is it?

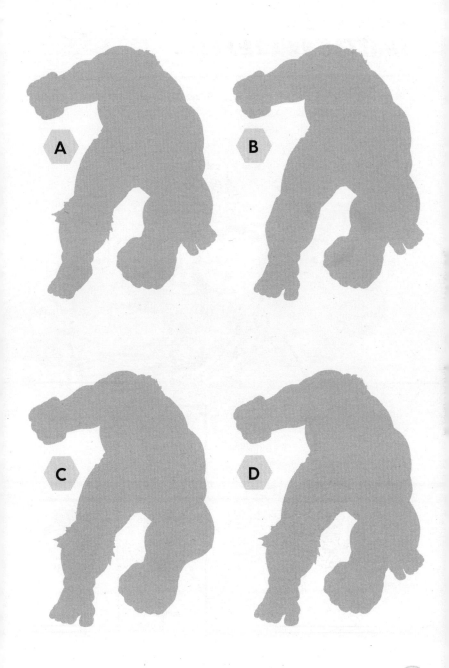

PUZZLE 21
SPATIAL AWARENESS

To move from one armoured suit to another in midair, while engaged in enemy combat, Tony Stark has to have great spatial awareness. Prove that you are just as mentally agile as Iron Man by studying the faces on the dice below. Then work out which one of the three-dimensional views on the opposite page is possible.

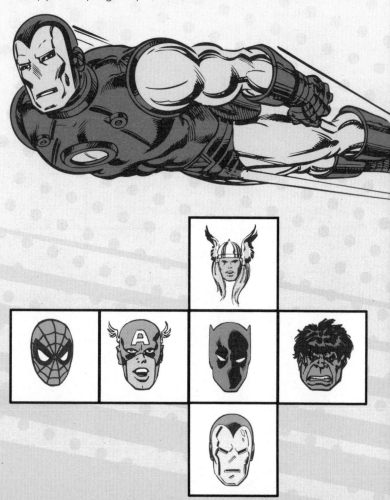

PUZZLE 22
WHO'S WHO HEROES?

It's time to name-check our favourite super heroes with their alter egos. Can you match the heroes on the left with the ordinary names they go by on the right?

1 **Cyclops**

2 **The Sub-Mariner**

3 **The Invisible Woman**

4 **Polaris**

5 **Silver Surfer**

6 **Spider-Woman**

7 **The Wasp**

8 **Winter Soldier**

9 **Ghost Rider**

To make it tougher, we've left an extra one, as an odd one out – can you spot that as well?

A Jessica Drew

B Susan Storm

C Scott Summers

D James Buchanan "Bucky" Barnes

E Lorna Dane

F Janet van Dyne

G Johnny Blaze

H Norrin Radd

PUZZLE 23
"I AM GROOT"

Thor took a class on Asgard, which is why he understands Groot. But not everyone does. To those who don't speak his language, it seems as though there's only one sentence in his vocabulary and it's always the same! This puzzle lists what he says in different languages around the world.

Can you match each phrase with the correct language?

ICH BIN GROOT	SPANISH
ÉN VAGYOK GROOT	GERMAN
JESTEM GROOT	FRENCH
EU SOU GROOT	HUNGARIAN
ADIM GROOT	TURKISH
WATASHI WA GURŪTODESU 私はグルートです	POLISH
YO SOY GROOT	JAPANESE
JE M'APPELLE GROOT	PORTUGUESE

Each shape contains four letters.
Can you make four names
of Asgardians by
taking one letter
from each shape,
starting from 1?

1

H O
T L

2

O
H D
E

3

L
I K
O

4

A
I R
N

PUZZLE 25
UNDERCOVER

Sometimes a hero (or a villain!) needs to go undercover to stay secret. Can you work out who is who from these curious names?

Clue: they are anagrams

1
DENIS PRAM

2
RT DORSAL

3
ASHTON

4
KERBY CUBANS

5
JENNY VEDANTA

6
BRINN ALCOTT

PUZZLE 26
NAME THAT COMIC

Can you help Iron Fist figure out all the titles of the following comics? We've left plenty of clues.

1 THE A_____ SPIDER-MAN

2 FANTASTIC F____

3 THE I_____ HULK

4 X-M__

5 THE INFINITY W__

6 THE I_____ GAUNTLET

7 SILVER S_____

8 SQUIRREL G____

9 DOCTOR S_____

10 THE SAVAGE S___-HULK

PUZZLE 27
WHO AM I?

One of the Guardians of the Galaxy has gone missing. Can you work out who it is from the letter clues below? We've filled in a few letters for you to get you started.

The right letter in the right place looks like this:

The right letter in the wrong place looks like this:

And if the letter is not in the word it looks like this:

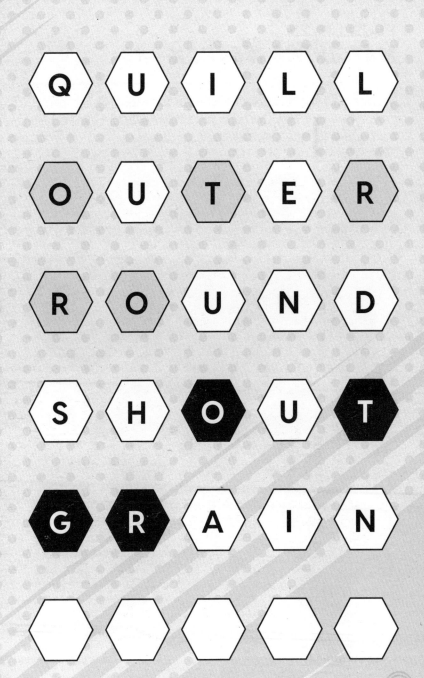

QUILL
OUTER
ROUND
SHOUT
GRAIN

PUZZLE 28
MATCH THE WEAPON

Heroes and villains alike are famous for wielding certain powerful weapons. Can you match the weapon to its user from the two lists opposite?

CAPTAIN AMERICA	INFINITY GAUNTLET
GORR THE GOD BUTCHER	VIBRANIUM STRIKE GAUNTLETS
LOKI	ALL-BLACK THE NECROSWORD
SHURI	WEB SHOOTERS
SPIDER-MAN	YAKA ARROWS
STAR-LORD	HAMMER
THANOS	SCEPTER
THOR	SHIELD
YONDU	ELEMENT GUN

Use your eagle eyes to spot five differences between these two images of the mighty Thor.

WORDSEARCH

Can you help Hawkeye find the characters, objects and places from the word list on the right, in the grid? They can be hidden horizontally, vertically or diagonally, and can be read from right to left, or from left to right.

ANT-MAN	IRON MAN	OKOYE
BULLSEYE	JUSTICE	PIXIE
EITRI	KRAVEN	SVARTALFHEIM
ELECTRO	LAUFEY	SWORD
FRIGGA	MANDARIN	TESSERACT
GAMMA	MIMIC	THANOS
HAWKEYE	NEBULA	

```
H A W K E Y E S F R I G G A E
M G A I T C L O U S R E E E Y
O M X U I M A N D A R I N I O
O I N T R K R A V E N J T T K
P T S E J O G H I K O L G R O
I U C S V A R T A L F H E I M
J N A A S G A R Y M A L I K N
A H O C R A L E L D E U N A M
M I M I C E C D K S Y Q F Q I
M J Y L D N S I I C M A U E Z
A U Z R E A D S C U O L I I Y
G A O R T C E L E O R U U I N
P W T K O A H S A T A B S R J
S B U L L S E Y E K N E R E V
R I R O N M A N A M T N A U Q
```

PUZZLE 31
WHO'S WHO VILLAINS?

How well do you know your villains? It's time to match the everyday names they hide behind, on the left, with their viciously villainous names on the right!

1. **Adrian Toomes**

2. **Tilda Johnson**

3. **Brock Rumlow**

4. **Bucky Barnes**

5. **Obadiah Stane**

6. **Otto Octavius**

7. **Darren Cross**

8. **Max Eisenhardt**

9. **Mark Scarlotti**

10. **Johann Schmidt**

To make it tougher, we've left an extra one,
as an odd one out – can you spot that as well?

A Ultron

B Whiplash

C Crossbones

D Nightshade

E Yellowjacket

F Iron Monger

G Magneto

H Vulture

I Doctor Octopus

J Red Skull

K Winter Soldier

PUZZLE 32
CODEWORD

Can you help Spider-Man crack the code to fill in the grid?
Each letter of the alphabet has a number assigned to it and
some are filled in for you. When it is finished a special answer
word will be revealed across the centre.

Key grid:

1	2	3	4	5	6	7	8	9	10	11	12	13
14	15	16	17 A	18	19	20	21	22	23	24	25	26

Main grid:

20	11	10	8	7	24	■	20 L	8 I	19 Z	17 A	1 R	9 D
18	■	5	■	17 A	■	8	■	7	■	25	■	17 A
23	18	4	7	14	■	1	■	9	1	8	24	1
25	■	8	■	17 A	21	18	4	1	■	13	■	23
12	17 A	16	■	10	■	7	■	17 A	21	8	14	11
17	■	■	■	13	■	26	■	■	1	■	■	■
2	17 A	7	9	17 A	21	17 A	15	8	21	18	22	22
■	■	18	■	■	■	14	■	1	■	■	■	17 A
18	14	13	24	1	■	1	■	18	■	20	17 A	7
4	■	3	■	18	7	8	18	7	■	17 A	■	9
14	2	17 A	7	6	■	18	■	21	8	15	24	1
6	■	1	■	4	■	14	■	17 A	■	24	■	17 A
18	16	1	8	24	7	■	17 A	7	14	1	17 A	20

59

PUZZLE 33
MISSING VOWELS

Can you work out the names of the famous female characters listed here? A super villain has removed all the vowels, making it tough – but not impossible – to work out who they are.

1 _M__R__CA CH_V__Z

2 BL__CK W_D_W

3 G_M_R_

4 J_N_ F_ST_R

5 MS. M__RV__L

6 J_N_T V_N DYN_

MULTIPLE CHOICE QUIZ

How well do you know your Marvel Universe? Put your knowledge to the test in this multiple choice quiz. The answers are there for you, just choose the correct one.

1

What was Stephen Strange's job before he had his accident?

A. Butcher

B. Dentist

C. Neurosurgeon

D. Rally driver

2

Which of these characters has also proven worthy of lifting Thor's hammer?

A. Captain America

B. Hulk

C. Tony Stark

D. Thanos

3

What "colour" is Wanda Maximoff – the _____ Witch?

A. Black

B. Green

C. Scarlet

D. Teal

4

What type of
creature is Rocket?

A. Fox

B. Hamster

C. Panda

D. Raccoon

5

What is
Kamala's (Ms. Marvel)
surname?

A. Jones

B. Kamalasson

C. Khalsa

D. Khan

6

Which of the
following is the name
of Thor's mother?

A. Freya

B. Frigga

C. Odin

D. Valkyrie

PUZZLE 35
SPATIAL AWARENESS

When it comes to aerial dexterity and committing to a movement, the Wasp rarely misses. How strong are you when it comes to spatial awareness? Look at the faces on the dice below and work out which one of the 3-D views on the opposite page is possible.

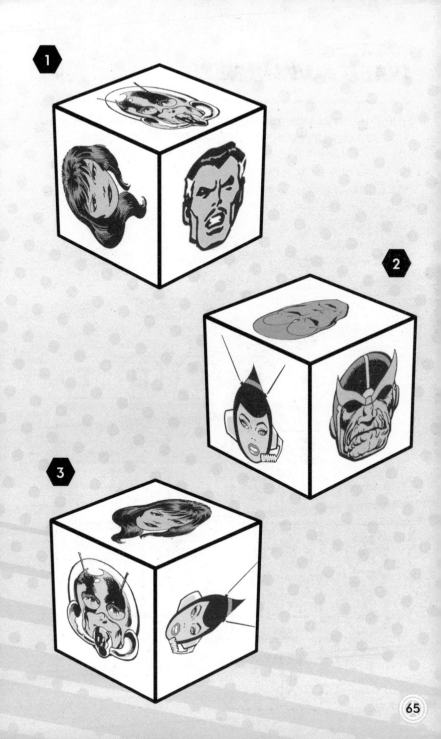

PUZZLE 36
PLACE A NUMBER

Fill in the empty boxes in the grid with the numbers 1, 2, 3, 4 and 5, always following the three rules:

A number must not appear more than once in a row.

A number must not appear more than once in a column.

A number must not appear more than once in each shaded shape.

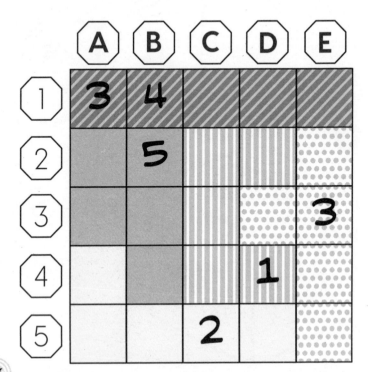

PUZZLE 37
BREAKOUT

Wanda Maximoff uses her formidable powers of mental manipulation to confound her foes. This time she has made you think you are locked up in the centre of a maze. Can you find your way out and break the spell?

PUZZLE 38
YNBW QUIZ

This is a quiz with only four possible answers:

| YES | NO | BLACK | WHITE |

Try not to get any wrong!

		YES	NO	BLACK	WHITE
1	Complete the super hero's name: _____ Panther				
2	Did Kamala Khan's parents emigrate from Pakistan?				
3	Was Peter Parker's mother a spider?				
4	What colour is Storm's hair?				
5	Complete Ava Ayala's alter ego name: _____ Tiger				
6	Was Jane Foster able to wield Mjolnir?				
7	What colour is Nick Fury's eye patch?				

PUZZLE 39
ODD ONE OUT

What's up Ant-Man? Can you help him work out which line is the odd one out, and why?

1

2

3

4

5

PUZZLE 40
IN THE SHADOWS

Pay attention! Only one of the shadows opposite is an exact match of the Scarlet Witch, but can you tell which one it is?

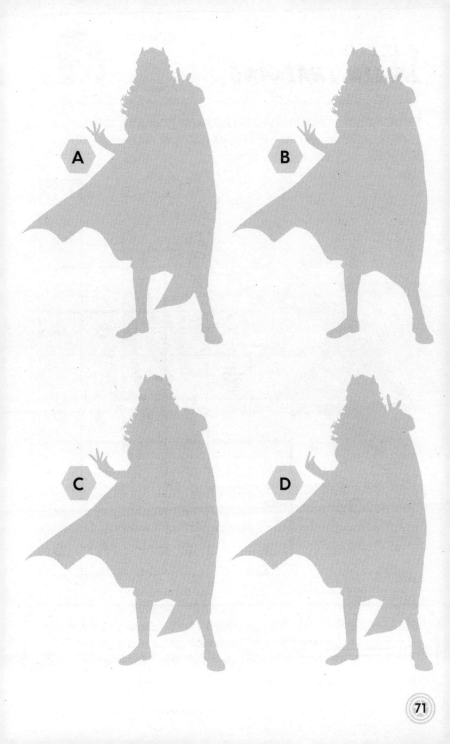

BRAIN TRAINING

Doctor Doom and Reed Richards have battled many times but Richards has always triumphed, often due to his superior intellect. Summon your powers of logic and deduction to complete this puzzle.

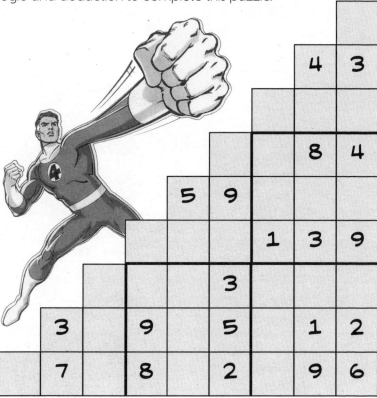

Fill in the grid with the numbers 1 to 9, following the rules that each number can only appear once in each 3 x 3 box and on the three edges of the triangle.

Each shield contains five letters. Can you make the names of five super heroes by taking one letter from each shield? Start with a letter in shield 1 and follow the order.

SPOT THE DIFFERENCE

How sharp-eyed are you? Take a close look at these two images of Hawkeye and see if you can spot five differences.

CLUED UP

Using the clues opposite, can you work out the identities of these eight characters?

1

_____

Human mother
Alien father
Gamora

2

_____

US Air Force
Kree
Superhuman strength

3

_____

Wakandan
Malice
Poison

4

_____

Orange
Rock-like
Strong

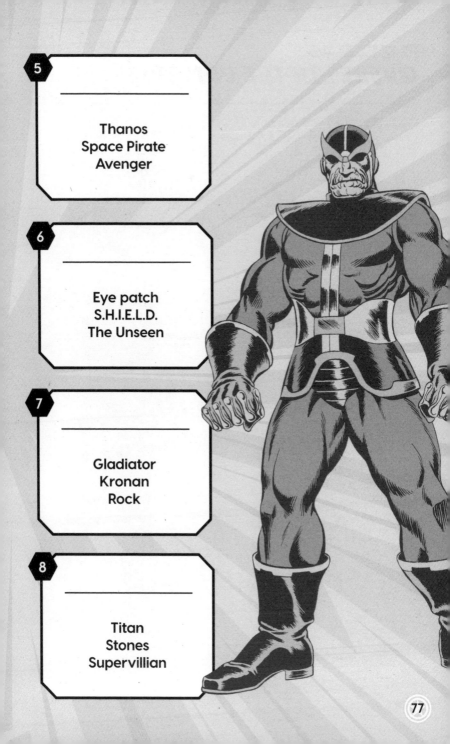

5

_____

Thanos
Space Pirate
Avenger

6

_____

Eye patch
S.H.I.E.L.D.
The Unseen

7

_____

Gladiator
Kronan
Rock

8

_____

Titan
Stones
Supervillian

WHERE... IN THE UNIVERSE?

Can you fill in the missing letters and work out the names of these Marvel Universe planets?

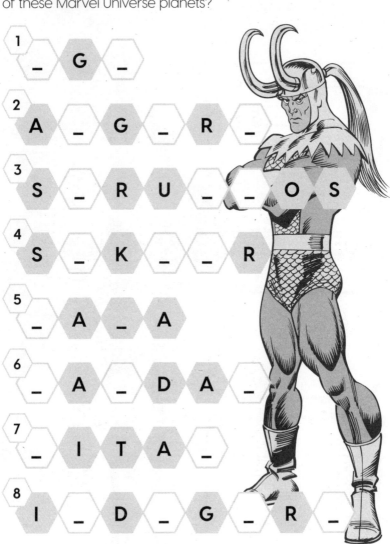

1. _ G _

2. A _ G _ R _

3. S _ R U _ _ O S

4. S _ K _ _ R

5. _ A _ A

6. _ A _ D A _

7. _ I T A _

8. I _ D _ G _ R _

THOR AND FRIENDS

Can you combine the word parts to create the names of five characters who are friends with Thor? Watch out – one of the names is actually two words!

HU

DRAL

ER

NE

FAN

VOL

HO

GG

STA

FO

ST

LK

JA

GUN

Hidden in the grid below are characters, objects and places, which are listed in the panel on the right. Can you find them? The words can be read up, down or across, and from right to left, or left to right.

```
K W A H K R A D G H D B R Y T
Y X N E G O S H U R I A O M H
N O O B N W J L S I S T N R O
N H S L A V K O G M O R A G R
I C E C L S U A V R L O N E K
L N M V E I L R T O A C H R I
B E A K I L U T I V T T A B E
O L J V S N I P E R O H A L A
G E N E S I S R N M S E O I M
B H H T A J S L T R P L C L L
O Y O X C A B U E R I E V G E
H R J S G Y X G W A M A S F D
M R Y E T O I E O A D P O T A
M A L E K I T H N G S E O L L
A R A H O L E U G I M R R Y B
```

BATROC THE LEAPER

BEAK

BLADE

CASSIE LANG

DARKHAWK

EGO

GENESIS

GHOST

HELEN CHO

HOBGOBLIN

HULK

ICEMAN

JOHN JAMESON

MAGIK

MALEKITH

MIGUEL OHARA

MORAG

RONAN

SHURI

STORM

TALOS

TEMPEST

THOR

VORMIR

WONG

PYRAMID POWER

Back in the lab, T'Challa and Shuri are busy testing some new tech toys for Black Panther. While they are occupied, can you work out the missing numbers from these two pyramids? Each number is the sum of the squares below it.

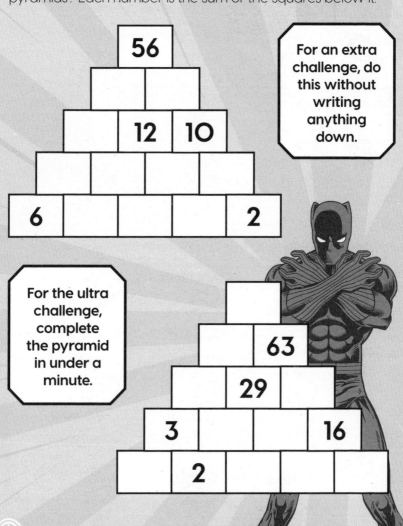

56

12 **10**

6 **2**

For an extra challenge, do this without writing anything down.

For the ultra challenge, complete the pyramid in under a minute.

63

29

3 **16**

2

PUZZLE 49
ODD ONE OUT

Can you work out which
line is the odd one out
and why?

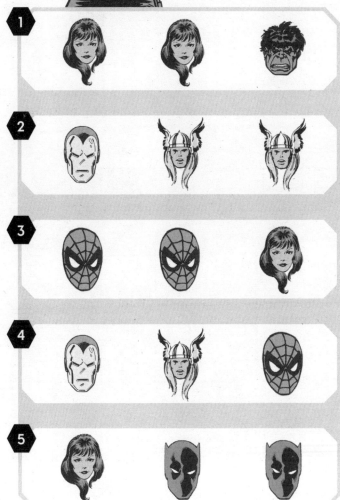

Spider-Man and Iron Man have swung into action, but can you crack the code to fill in the grid? Each letter of the alphabet has a number assigned to it and some are filled in for you. When it is finished a special answer will be revealed across the centre.

Code-breaker key

1	2	3	4	5	6	7	8	9 B	10	11	12	13
14	15	16	17	18 A	19	20	21	22	23	24	25	26

Grid

4	24	1	10	2	13	■	11 Q	5 U	18 A	4 S	18 A	1 R
24	■	13	■	1	■	9 B	■	16	■	21	■	14
1	18 A	25	9 B	13	18 A	5	■	23	1	18 A	15	16
18 A	■	20	■	13	■	21	■	20	■	7	■	18 A
16	13	6	5	4	■	19	20	16	3	23	20	16
3	■	■	■	20	■	10	■	■	■	13	■	■
13	7	20	22	18 A	8	9	1	18 A	12	7	13	10
■	■	24	■	■	■	18 A	■	21	■	■	■	14
15	1	13	21	19	13	1	■	18 A	26	20	18 A	16
18 A	■	25	■	18 A	■	16	■	12	■	16	■	1
3	7	20	24	17	■	13	7	13	21	24	1	14
13	■	4	■	18 A	■	4	■	25	■	1	■	3
4	8	13	18 A	1	4	■	21	10	9 B	14	1	3

Look at the list of words on the right and see if you can help the Hulk find the characters, objects and places listed in the grid below. The words can be read horizontally, vertically or diagonally, and from right to left, or from left to right.

```
S S X A Q A F P C R A K L U H
A O I M Y D F S U C V X M A N
K R B O W I O D X I E I I A N
A E G R U S N H A T K Y L G W
A S G A R D A B C O R S A I R
R T O R O R M W L R T L N O B
O L N T U O O Q O S A M O J O
H T A E D C R F G N I W D E R
T O O R G C A F I S G U A D V
S F N T Y A H K N I G S L E Y
A K R I M A S H A P A D N A R
D A N G E R A U P Y U Y R R A
Y L N E S I T N A M H T I T E
R A O N J E A N R G E Y F H P
M H F L O W N A M I S R E S S
```

ACCORDS   LUIS   SIF

ASGARD   MAW   SPEAR

BOW   MILANO   THOR

CORSAIR   NATASHA   TORO

ROMANOFF

EROS   TYR

OYA

GROOT   WONG

REDWING

HALA   YAKA

SAKAAR

HULK   YAO

SERSI

LOKI

COMPLETE THE COMICS

Can you complete the comic and character titles?

1 SABRE

2 GHOST

3 STAR

4 EDGE OF SPIDER-

5 MIRACLE

6 THE MIGHTY THOR: AVENGERS

7 CAPTAIN AMERICA

RE

8 IMMORTAL

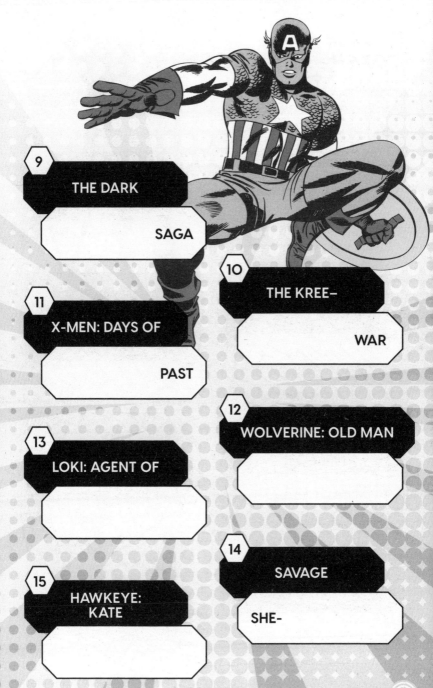

9 THE DARK

SAGA

10 THE KREE–

WAR

11 X-MEN: DAYS OF

PAST

12 WOLVERINE: OLD MAN

13 LOKI: AGENT OF

14 SAVAGE

SHE-

15 HAWKEYE: KATE

PUZZLE 53
ESCAPE THE RAFT

Captain America has made his way into prison to help his Avenger friends escape. Starting from the centre of the maze, can you help him figure a way out? Beware – the road is long and you'll need plenty of patience to make a successful bid for freedom.

Each shield contains five letters. Can you make five names of characters by taking one letter from each shield? Start with a letter in shield 1, then shield 2 and follow the order.

ODD IRON MAN OUT

You have 30 seconds to spot which one of these Iron Man helmets does not match the others.

Complete this in 10 seconds for a mega challenge.

PUZZLE 56
STONE PLACEMENT

Four Infinity Stones are missing from the grid below and you need to find them. To help you locate these potentially dangerous objects, the numbers in the grid show how many stones are adjacent to that square, including diagonally. Good luck!

		1	
			2
2	4		
	2		

Can you help Spider-Man make five names of characters by taking one letter only from each shield? Start with a letter in shield 1, then shield 2 and follow the order.

1

L
H J
N
T

2

A
O H
O
U

3

O
L V
N K

4

I
K E
A R

95

PUZZLE 58
CODEWORD

Venom is on the rampage! Can you crack the code to fill in the grid? Each letter of the alphabet has a number assigned to it and some are filled in for you. When it is finished a special answer word will be revealed across the centre.

Key grid:

1	2	3	4	5	6	7	8	9	10	11	12	13
14	15	16	17	18 H	19	20	21	22	23	24	25	26

Puzzle grid:

8	4	22	24	4	16	■	20 Q	25 U	10 I	1 V	12 E	9 R
3	■	3	■	11	■	8	■	14	■	12	■	25
19	10	11	12	9	10	4	■	22	3	9	17	19
12	■	9	■	4	■	6	■	25	■	23	■	19
17	16	4	19	18 H	■	12	14	23	2	10	14	12
18 H	■	■	■	4	■	19	■	■	7	■	23	
■	8	10	6	6	13	18 H	25	5	19	3	14	■
22	■	9	■	■	■	25	■	4	■	■	■	18 H
3	9	3	23	25	14	5	■	21	16	3	5	4
19	■	14	■	14	■	19	■	21	■	22	■	9
6	10	6	10	22	■	3	10	16	2	12	16	16
10	■	4	■	16	■	14	■	12	■	4	■	12
22	3	14	1	12	15	■	26	9	12	14	21	13

97

PUZZLE 59
SYMBOL SWEEP

You'll need the quick thinking and observation skills of Black Panther to find a pattern in this test. Find the following sequence of four symbols in the grid below as quickly as you can. It could be vertical, horizontal or diagonal. How many times does the sequence appear?

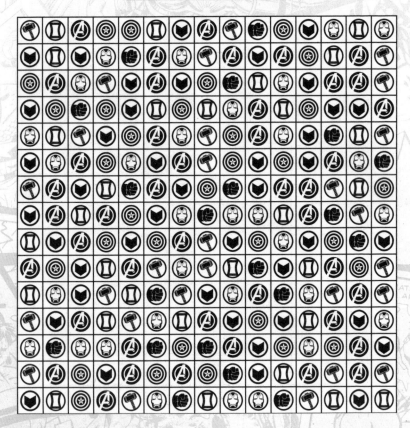

Fill in the empty boxes in the grid with the numbers 1, 2, 3, 4, 5 and 6, always following the three rules:

A number must not appear more than once in a row.

A number must not appear more than once in a column.

A number must not appear more than once in each shaded shape.

	A	B	C	D	E	F
1					4	3
2	5	2		3		
3	4					2
4		6				
5			5		1	
6			1	6		

Enchantress has used her spellbinding powers to remove all the vowels, making it tough – but not impossible – to work out the names of the villains listed here.

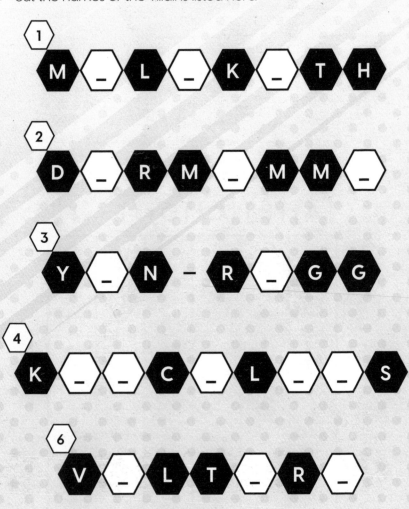

1. M _ L _ K _ T H

2. D _ R M _ M M _

3. Y _ N - R _ G G

4. K _ _ _ C _ L _ _ _ S

6. V _ L T _ R _

5

M R

F _ N T _ S T _ C

PUZZLE 62
IN THE SHADOWS

Can you tell which of the shadows is an exact image
of the Wasp? To add a sting to this puzzle, we've rotated
the shadows - stay sharp!

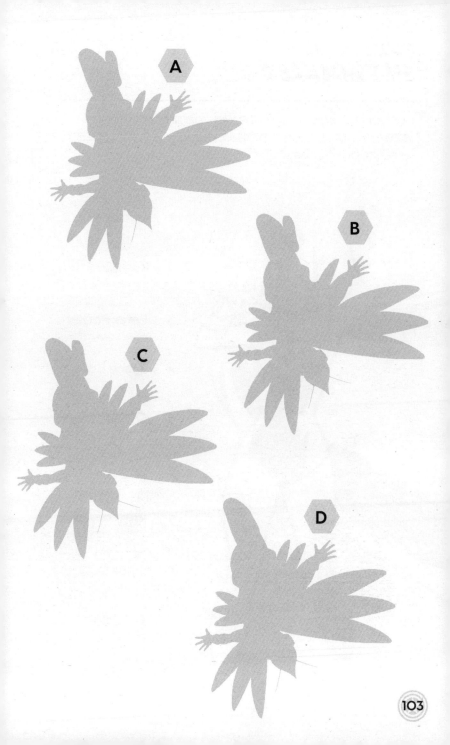

MATCHMAKER

Can you match the super heroes to their other halves? Take one name from the left-hand page and find their friend or partner on the right to match them up.

1   **Cyclops**

2   **Kamala Khan**

3   **Peter Parker**

4   **Bruce Banner**

5   **Scarlet Witch**

6   **Rogue**

7   **Kitty Pryde**

8   **Peter Quill**

9   **T'Challa**

10   **Carol Danvers**

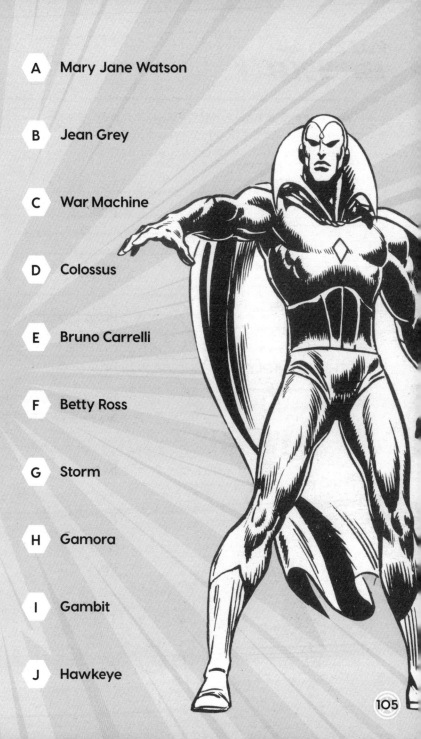

A Mary Jane Watson

B Jean Grey

C War Machine

D Colossus

E Bruno Carrelli

F Betty Ross

G Storm

H Gamora

I Gambit

J Hawkeye

PUZZLE 64
ASSEMBLE!

Can you match the words below with those opposite to 'assemble' the characters?

SILVER

INVISIBLE

HUMAN

FLASH

SQUIRREL

BLACK

THUNDERBOLT

IRON

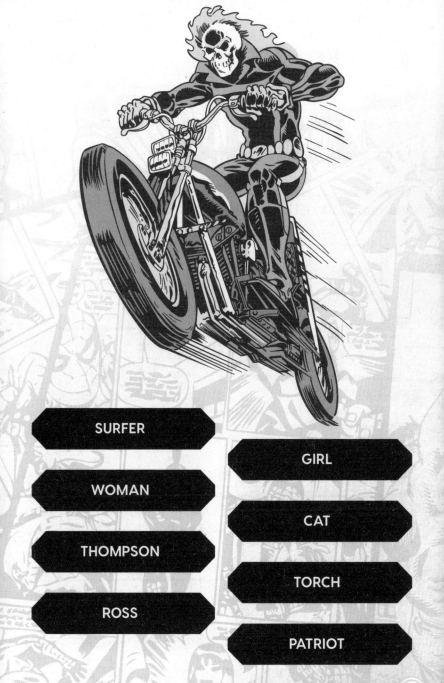

SURFER

WOMAN

THOMPSON

ROSS

GIRL

CAT

TORCH

PATRIOT

PUZZLE 65
MEMORY MASTER

Doctor Strange has a mind bending test for you. Each number in the grid represents a symbol, as shown opposite. Spend one minute memorising the symbols, then cover them up.

Now summon your powers of recall and use the symbols to fill in the empty grid opposite.

1	2	4	1
2	3	1	3
1	3	2	2
4	1	2	1

1 = Ɛ

2 = #

3 = %

4 = /

PUZZLE 66
PYRAMID POWER

Ant-Man is in the lab, fighting with Darren Cross and the Wasp. While they are busy, can you work out the missing numbers from these two pyramids? Each number is the sum of the squares below it.

113

27

11

4   9

For an extra challenge, do this without writing anything down.

For the ultra challenge, complete the pyramid in under a minute.

61   64

32

13

12   9

XAVIER'S RIDDLE

Professor X, at the School for Gifted Youngsters, has set his pupils a challenge. Can you help them solve it?

You have four books and three boxes, one small, one medium, one large.

You must store the books in the boxes, according to the following rules:

The large box must contain twice as many books as the medium one.

The medium box must contain twice as many books as the small one.

All the books must be stored in boxes.

Each box can fit inside the box that is bigger.

Where should you place the books (and the boxes)?

PUZZLE 68
ENTRY CODE

Taskmaster needs to break into the Raft maximum security prison, but the entry codes have been changed. He will have to work out the new combination. Fortunately, the new 9-digit code only uses the numbers 1 to 9. Can you work out the code for Sentry using the numbers only once?

It's not easy – first you have to work out the sums below.

Cross off the numbers in the chart below as you go:

1   2   3   4   ✗   6   7   8   ✗

	+		−	5	=	3
+		−		−		
	+		+		=	8
+		+		+		
9	−		+		=	10
=		=		=		
15		10		12		

TRUE OR FALSE?

Can you tell whether these statements are true or false?

1. Captain America has never had a fight with Iron Man.

2. Thor has a sister named Aldrif Odinsdottir, known as Angela.

3. White Vision is made of synthetic materials.

4. Thor is the only one to ever lift his hammer, Mjolnir.

5. There is a group (and a comic) called The West Coast Avengers.

6. Wolverine's claws are made of Vibranium.

7. Doctor Doom's full name is Victor Von Doom.

8. Doctor Strange's first name is Eric.

CODEWORD

Iron Man needs your help! Can you crack the code and fill in the grid? Each letter of the alphabet has a number assigned to it and some are filled in for you. When it is finished a special answer word will be revealed across the centre.

| 1 | 2 | 3 | 4 | 5 | 6 | 7 | 8 | 9 | 10 | 11 | 12 | 13 S |
| 14 | 15 | 16 | 17 | 18 | 19 | 20 | 21 | 22 | 23 | 24 | 25 | 26 |

11	8	4	22	7	6	■	13 S	20	16	1	8	13 S
7	■	12	■	3	■	18	■	18	■	16	■	10
23	16	19	19	16	22	7	■	16	8	19	7	19
7	■	11	■	26	■	3	■	26	■	22	■	16
22	21	7	19	7	■	8	19	8	6	8	14	1
8	■	■	■	2	■	23	■	■	■	23	■	■
10	21	16	19	2	7	13 S	17	16	3	8	7	19
■	■	8	■	■	■	9	■	1	■	■	■	16
20	16	19	26	8	19	6	■	7	15	19	12	1
16	■	4	■	6	■	23	■	25	■	14	■	12
13 S	20	16	24	8	■	7	17	14	19	26	16	23
22	■	19	■	12	■	9	■	8	■	2	■	6
7	5	7	10	22	16	■	16 A	23 N	11 G	7 E	2 L	16 A

115

PUZZLE 71
INCOGNITO!

Some characters have gone deep undercover and disguised their names. Can you work out who is who?

Clue: they are all anagrams.

1 CAVA IMPLANTER

2 THOR MANCHU

3 NORBERT SHOULDST

4 POWERS ADMIN

5 WIMBLE INVASION

6 ALF HOSPMONTHS

7 AMOS SMELLIER

8 DUTCH HEADWORK

9 HOOPS CULLIN

10 RICKY FUN

PUZZLE 72
MULTIPLE CHOICE

Can you get the questions right in this multiple choice quiz?
The answers are there for you, just choose the correct one.

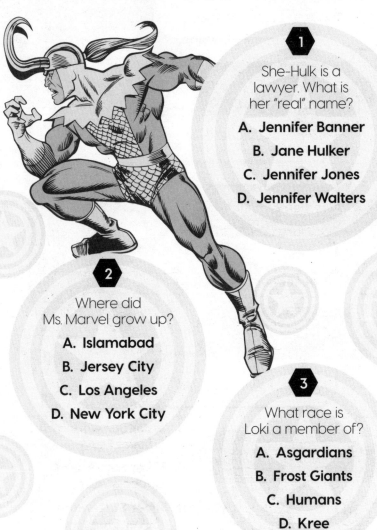

1

She-Hulk is a lawyer. What is her "real" name?

A. Jennifer Banner

B. Jane Hulker

C. Jennifer Jones

D. Jennifer Walters

2

Where did Ms. Marvel grow up?

A. Islamabad

B. Jersey City

C. Los Angeles

D. New York City

3

What race is Loki a member of?

A. Asgardians

B. Frost Giants

C. Humans

D. Kree

4

Which of these is an adopted daughter of Thanos?

A. Peggy Carter

B. Ego

C. Gamora

D. Gargantos

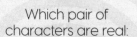

5

The Sorcerer Supreme uses the Eye of what?

A. Agamemnon

B. Aggro

C. Agamotto

D. The Tiger

6

Which pair of characters are real:

A. Silver Surfer and Silver Sable

B. Silver Surfer and Silver Fox

C. Silver Surfer and Super Surfer

D. Silver Surfer and Silver Blade

PUZZLE 73
WORDSEARCH

Check the word list opposite and help Medusa unlock the places, characters and objects hidden in the grid. The words can be read horizontally, vertically or diagonally, from right to left, or from left to right.

ARES	JARVIS	RAMPAGE
CLEA	JULIUS	REPULSOR
DRAX	MAGMA	ROGUE
DUST	MEDUSA	SHIELD
GAUNTLET	ONSLAUGHT	TIGRA
HELA	ORB	TITAN
HOGUN	PRODIGY	YONDU
HYDRA	PYRO	ZABU

```
H O G U N A T I T R F B P W M
U B R A M P A G E A G A Y O E
S Y R Y U D U B A Z C Q R D D
K G O O H N N B Y A R T O E U
B I J N C I T I R K I I D X S
O D J D O Y T L M R I G V O A
N O S U G R E F E C M R L A C
S R H G L U E R H T N A G I A
L P I K S I T W T C A M G A M
A M E Q M O U R O S L U P E R
U L L L Y A E S W P U E D U K
G M D E N L E T E B K D A G A
H B B O O E S M C E U C M O O
T E N I V H C N S Y X X A R D
E H Y D R A K H S I V R A J W
```

Time to put your sharp eyes to the test. Can you spot five differences between these two images of Black Widow?

WHO AM I?

The right letter in the right place looks like this:

O

Raise the alarm, one of the Guardians of the Galaxy has gone missing!

The right letter in the wrong place looks like this:

R

Can you work out who it is from the letter clues below?

And if the letter is not in the word it looks like this:

T

C	H	A	R	M	S

Q	U	A	R	T	O

T	R	O	O	P	S

G	R	I	P	P	Y

HIDDEN VILLAINS

Some of your favourite anti-heroes have gone rogue and disguised their names. Can you work out who is who?

Clue: they are anagrams

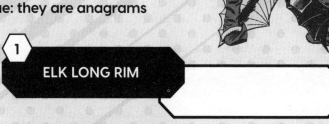

1 ELK LONG RIM

2 MOMMA DUR

3 RON LUT

4 XIPHOID TRAMMING

5 HANS OT

6 KEITH LAM

7 TODD COMORO

8 YUKS LAWLESS

9 DERWIN SERTOLI

10 OWEN AMBY

11 CLOVIS VAGUER

12 PHIL HAWS

PUZZLE 77
WHAT'S MY NAME?

Sharpen your pencil – it's time to fill in the blanks and work out who's who.

To make it extra difficult, a hyphen counts as one letter in this puzzle. For example, Ant-Man would be a 7-letter word.

1. A _ N _ M
   Z _ L _

2. W _ _ P _ A _ H

3. _ A _ E R _ A C E

4. _ _ C K
   _ _ R Y

5 C _ _ S S B _ _ _ S

6 _ _ _ _ A
_ I L L

7 S T _ _
_ O _ D

8 N _ _ A
_ R I M _

9 _ A _
_ _ _ S _ N

10 _ _ I D _ _ _
_ A _

TRUE OR FALSE?

Can you tell whether these statements are true or false?

1 Sersi is the leader of the Deviants.

2 Stan Lee co-created Spider-Man.

3 Pym Particles are named after Hank Pym.

4 "Happy" Hogan's middle name is Joseph.

5 Drax was once a human named Arthur Douglas.

6 Malekith is a Kree.

7 James Rhodes is War Machine.

8 Mockingbird is married to Hawkeye.

Steve Rogers, like any good soldier, has been trained to make his way across a minefield safely. Try to work out the locations of all 30 mines using the number clues in the grid. The number tells you how many mines there are in adjacent squares, including diagonally.

			2	3	2			
	1		2				1	
		2					3		1
		3			3				
2		4		4		3	3	2	
		5	3			2			
		4						1	
2		5					2		
	2			4	4		4		
		3	2			2			

PUZZLE 80
MISSING VOWELS

Can you work out the names of the famous characters listed here? Someone removed all the vowels, making it tough – though not impossible – to work out who they are.

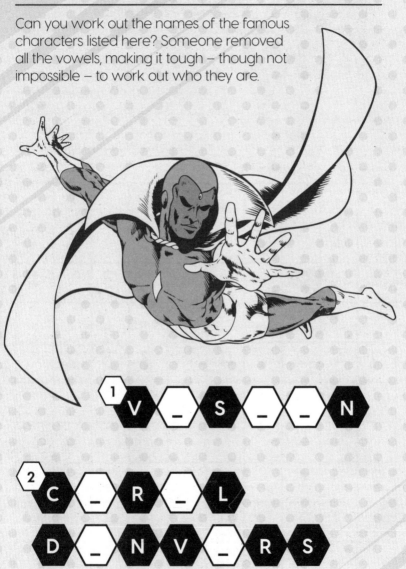

1. V _ S _ _ N

2. C _ R _ L
   D _ N V _ R S

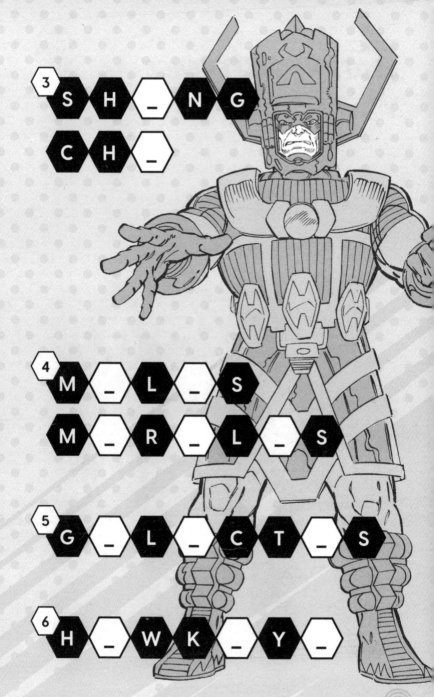

3. SH_NG CH_

4. M_L_S
M_R_L_S

5. G_L_CT_S

6. H_WK_Y_

Something's up, down or sideways with Doctor Strange! Turn the book and see if you can spot ten differences between these two images.

PUZZLE 82
SHIELD WORDS

Each of Captain America's shields contains six letters. Can you make six names of characters by taking one letter from each shield? Start with a letter in shield 1, then shield 2 and follow the order.

3

4

136

1

2

5

6

Captain America needs you to crack the code and fill in the grid. Are you ready? Each letter of the alphabet has a number assigned to it and some are filled in for you. When it is finished a special answer word will be revealed across the centre.

Codeword

Key grid:

1	2	3	4	5 T	6	7	8	9	10	11	12	13
14	15	16	17	18	19	20	21	22	23	24	25	26

Main grid:

9	25	8	14	14	23	■	17	18	4	25	9	4
11	■	22	■	1	■	4	■	24	■	8	■	13
4	7	1	18	3	6	12	■	19	6	24	19	4
4	■	26	■	14	■	9	■	1	■	19	■	9
5 T	18	5 T	8	3	■	4	20	4	25	4	5 T	5 T
8	■	■	■	18	■	21	■	■	■	8	■	■
11	6	16	8	25	22	5 T	11	4	22	1	9	2
■	■	25	■	■	■	18	■	3	■	■	■	8
8	2	18	11	18	25	6	■	22	25	8	16	26
15	■	14	■	3	■	3	■	14	■	24	■	26
5 T	8	26	6	10	■	8	20	8	22	8	25	8
4	■	4	■	4	■	26	■	24	■	15	■	25
9 C	6 O	23 Y	6 O	5 T	4 E	■	19	4	22	4	9	2

139

PUZZLE 84
MEMORY MASTER

Rocket Raccoon has a tough challenge for you. Each number in the grid represents a symbol, as shown opposite. Spend one minute memorising the symbols, then cover them up.

Now summon your powers of recall and use the symbols to fill in the empty grid opposite.

2	4	2	3	2
3	1	2	1	5
2	1	3	2	4
3	4	3	4	2
5	3	4	5	1

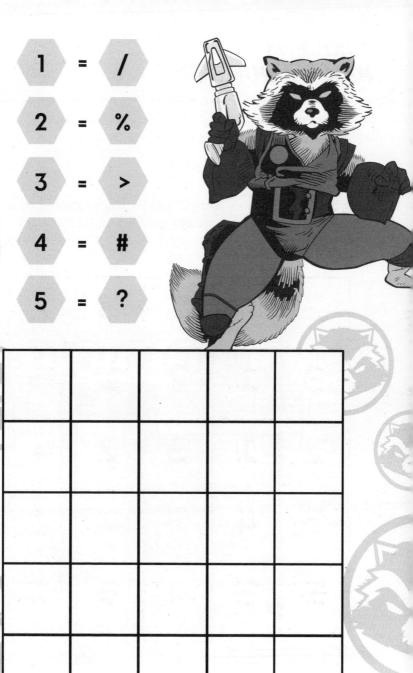

PUZZLE 85
PLACE A NUMBER

Fill in the empty boxes in the grid with the numbers
1, 2, 3, 4, 5 and 6, always following the three rules:

A number must not appear more than once in a row.

A number must not appear more than once in a column.

A number must not appear more than once in each shaded shape.

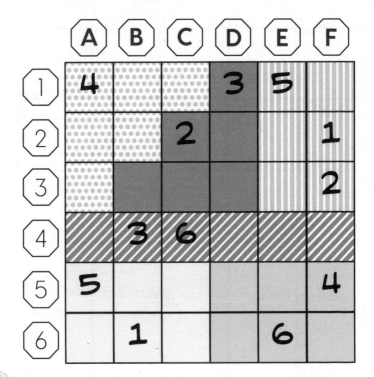

Tony Stark is locked out of his computer because he forgot the password. He knows it is on one of the pieces of paper he left in the lab, but he can't remember which one. The password appears on only one of the pieces of paper, can you find it?

Alpha

Ant-Man

Albert

Abyss

Astra

Albert

Anaconda

Angela

Avalanche

Astra

Anelle

Anaconda

Avalanche

Ant-Man

Alpha

Abyss

Anelle

PUZZLE 87
PLACEMENT

Malekith's ships are extremely hard to follow, even for the all-seeing Heimdall. Thor and his allies need to know the locations of all those ships. Using the number clues, can you plot the whereabouts of the enemy ships? The numbers in the grid refer to how many ships are in an adjacent square (including diagonally). There are 20 ships in the grid – hurry!

	1						3	
					3			
2		2		1		2	3	
					2			
	2		1			2		
			2		2			
	2	4	2					
		2				2		
2	2		4		3		2	
	3		2		2			

MARVEL ACROSTIC

Can you fill in the missing letters of this puzzle?

S   **SPIDER-MAN**

P   _ _ _ _ _ _ _ _ _ _ _   Spidey's alter-ego

I   _ _ _ _ _   _ _ _   Tony Stark

D   _ _ _ _ _ _ _ _ _ _ _   Stephen Strange

E   _ _ _ _ _ _ _ _   also known as White Queen

R   _ _ _ _ _ _   Anna Marie of the X-Men

M   _ _ _ _ _ _ _ _   Professor X's enemy

A   _ _ _ _-_ _ _ _   A tiny hero sometimes

N   _ _ _ _ _ _ _ _   Director of S.H.I.E.L.D.

PUZZLE 89
WHO AM I?

One of the Guardians of the Galaxy has gone missing. Can you help Star-Lord work out who it is from the letter clues below?

The right letter in the right place looks like this:

O

The right letter in the wrong place looks like this:

R

And if the letter is not in the word it looks like this:

A

COFFIN

SQUAWK

JUMBLE

CREASE

CRANKY

TRACKS

Each of these super heroes has a matching symbol, apart from one. Can you find the super hero without a match?

PUZZLE 91
INTERSTELLAR TRAVEL

Get your ship to the other side of the galaxy by drawing a single, continuous line (not diagonally) from point A to point B in the grid. The numbers next to the grid tell you how many squares in that row or column will be taken up by the line.

A										1
										1
										4
										8
										3
										7
										4
										7
										3
									B	5

8 5 1 6 3 4 1 5 3 7

If there's one place where you can see the effect of strength in numbers, it's in an ant colony. In this puzzle, you need to join up all the ants (represented by the dots) with one single line. You cannot make a diagonal link and each ant can only have two lines. We've added a few lines to get you started: now get busy!

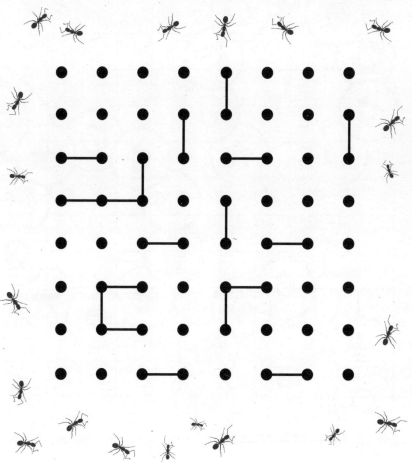

PUZZLE 93
VISION'S CHALLENGE

This challenge has been set by Vision. Carefully study the five groups. You have 30 seconds to work out which two groups contain exactly the same symbols.

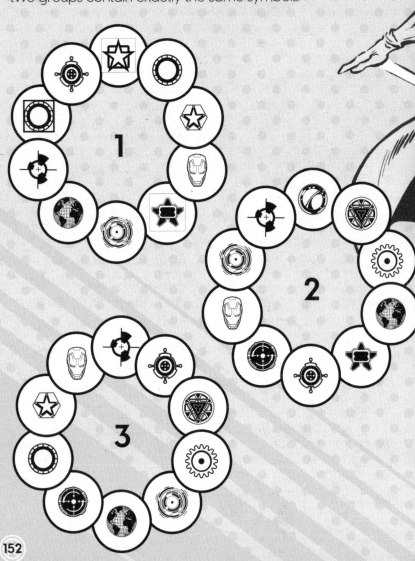

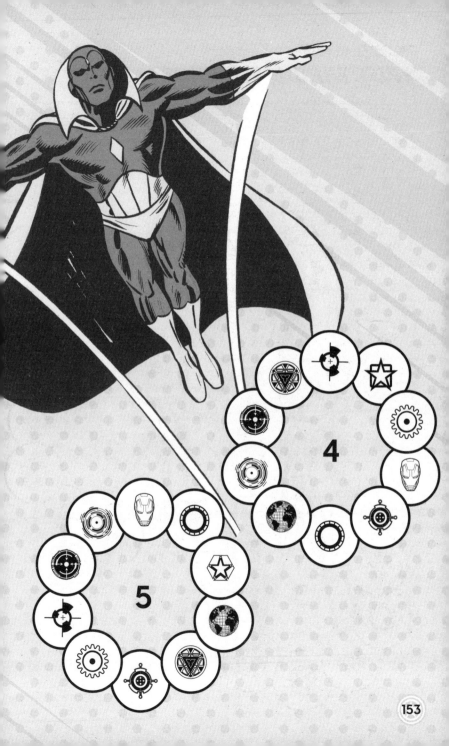

SPOT THE DIFFERENCE

How amazing are your powers of observation? Put them to the test and see if you can spot ten differences between these two images of Vision.

QUOTE QUIZ

Can you complete the quotes and match each one to its character?

"It's clobberin' _____"

NAMOR

"By the Hoary Hosts of _____!"

"To me, my _____"

DOCTOR STRANGE

"My _____-sense is tingling"

THE HUMAN TORCH

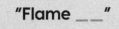

"Flame ___"

SPIDER-MAN

"By _____'s Beard!"

THE THING

"Imperius ____!"

THOR

THE SILVER SURFER

NAME THAT CHARACTER

Black Panther needs you! Can you identify the characters from the clues below?

1 Engineer | Clever kid | Rocket-propelled skateboard

2 New Warriors | Bubbles | Robbie Baldwin

3 Great Lakes Avengers | Tail | Doreen Green

4 Roderick Kingsley | Goblin War! | Glider

5 Doctor | Bendy | Scientist

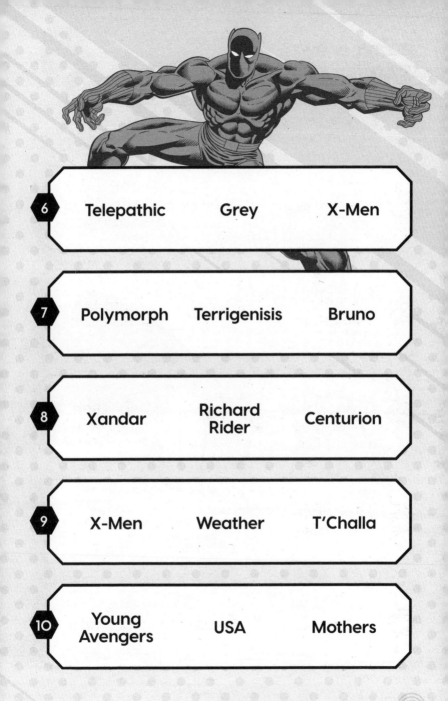

6. Telepathic   Grey   X-Men

7. Polymorph   Terrigenisis   Bruno

8. Xandar   Richard Rider   Centurion

9. X-Men   Weather   T'Challa

10. Young Avengers   USA   Mothers

TIMED ANALYSIS

When Jennifer Walters is working on a case she looks carefully at all the evidence. Can you help her with this one? You have 30 seconds to work out which two contain exactly the same symbols.

A

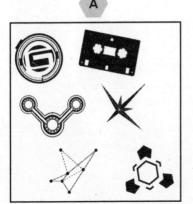

B

C

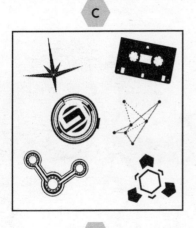

D

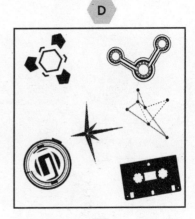

E

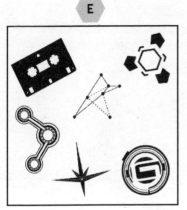

F

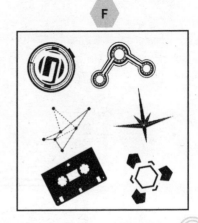

PUZZLE 98
MACRO VISION

Do you think you're an observation super hero? Crack this puzzle and find out. Only two of the ants on these pages are identical, but which two?

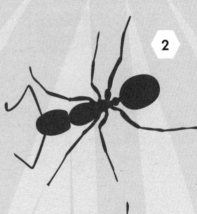

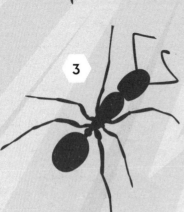

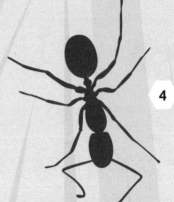

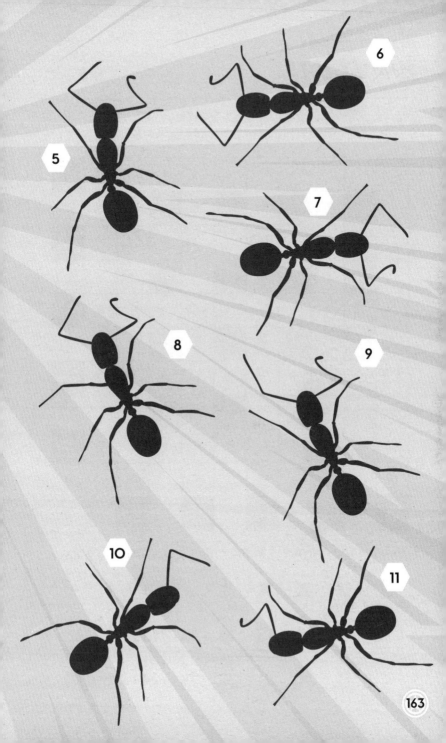

PUZZLE 99
SUM IT UP

Can you fill in the grid below so that all the calculations are correct, using each number from 1 to 25 once only?

23	+		x		−		+	19	=	411
−		x		−		+		x		
	÷	4	−	20	+		x		=	12
x		−		x				−		
			x		−	10	−		=	−16
+		−		−		+		+		
13	+		+	3	+		+		=	66
+		+		−		−		÷		
	−		x		−		÷	2	=	−94
=		=		=		=		=		
56		108		7		38		93		

Cross off the numbers in the chart below as you go:

1 ✗ ✗ ✗ 5 6 7 8 9

✗ 11 12 ✗ 14 15 16 17 18

✗ ✗ 21 22 ✗ 24 25

PUZZLE 100
PLACE A NUMBER

Fill in the empty boxes in the grid with the numbers
1, 2, 3, 4, 5, 6 and 7 always following the three rules:

A number must not appear more than once in a row.

A number must not appear more than once in a column.

A number must not appear more than once in each shaded shape.

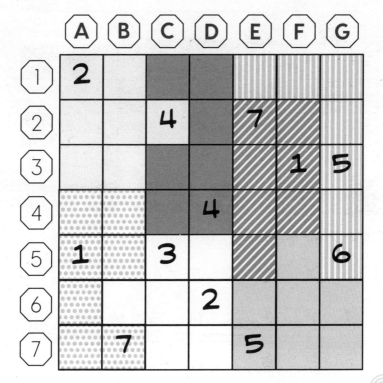

THE ANSWERS

Puzzle 1
SPEED TEST
1. Wanda Maximoff
2. Ultron
3. Spider-Man
4. Natasha Romanoff

Puzzle 2
ANT-MAZE

Puzzle 3
WHO AM I?
Shuri

Puzzle 4
IN THE SHADOWS
D is the correct shadow.

Puzzle 5
LAB WORK

87

42 45

19 23 22

8 11 12 10

2 6 5 7 3

Puzzle 6
BUILD A HERO!
1. Falcon
2. Magneto
3. Groot
4. Shuri
5. Valkyrie

Puzzle 7
WHO'S WHO HEROES?
1–G
2–D
3–H
4–B
5–C
6–F
7–A
8–I
9–J
10–E
Donald Blake is the extra name.

Puzzle 8
IN THE SHADOWS
B is the correct shadow.

Puzzle 9
WEIGH-IN
One hand should contain 3, 4, 5. The other has 1, 2, 9.

Puzzle 10
PLACE A NUMBER

2	4	5	1	3
1	2	3	5	4
4	1	2	3	5
3	5	1	4	2
5	3	4	2	1

Puzzle 11
ORDER!
1–D, 2–B, 3–E, 4–C
5–A

Puzzle 12
COMICS CREW
1. CAPTAIN MARVEL
2. IRON MAN
3. THOR
4. SPIDER-MAN
5. MAGNETO

Puzzle 13
PICTURE THIS
Spider Man x 6
Black Panther x 6
Black Widow x 6
Iron Man x 6
Captain America x 6

Puzzle 14
BUZZ WORDSEARCH

```
B R S R K S M E R U T A S T A
R O I H Y U M K O R A T H R P
O K L S I P A K N H E P M S R
B O B L R E T H A F S O A T T
S T A F F R L T N E R W C H E
J O S E P H F D T P E E G H P
L A Y D D E T A H T S R I K E
M C E W O R R A E T D F N Q C
B A T S T O O S A E U T E S S
A L F H B N U J C N F L M X T
K A I M A R N K C A R G A S K
U X N N T M A G U L D N N J A
C V E U K H M V S P D N I D O
U H R E N K R E A T N A M L
X E D E C A P S R E P Y H W C
```

Puzzle 15
SPOT THE DIFFERENCE

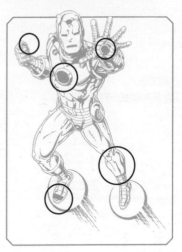

Puzzle 16
MULTIPLE CHOICE
1–A, 2–C, 3–C, 4–D,
5–D, 6–D

Puzzle 17
UNDERCOVER
1. Captain America
2. Iron Man
3. Carol Danvers
4. Pepper Potts
5. Jane Foster
6. Bruce Banner
7. Mantis
8. Valkyrie

Puzzle 18
STARS AND STRIPES
Seven red stripes; six white stripes; 50 stars. The 13 stripes represent the 13 founding states and there is one star for each current state.

Puzzle 19
PYRAMID POWER

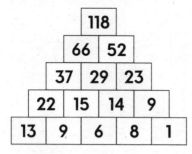

Puzzle 20
IN THE SHADOWS
D is the correct shadow.

Puzzle 21
SPATIAL AWARENESS
Only 2 is possible.

Puzzle 22
WHO'S WHO HEROES?
1–C, 3–B, 4–E, 5–H,
6–A, 7–F, 8–D, 9–G
The Sub-Mariner is the odd one out.

Puzzle 23
"I AM GROOT"
Ich bin Groot = German
Én vagyok Groot = Hungarian
Jestem Groot = Polish
Eu sou Groot = Portuguese
Adim Groot = Turkish
Watashi wa Gurūtodesu / 私はグルートです = Japanese
Yo soy Groot = Spanish
Je m'appelle Groot = French

Puzzle 24
FOUR-UP
THOR, ODIN, LOKI, HELA

Puzzle 25
UNDERCOVER
1. Spider-Man
2. Star-Lord
3. Thanos
4. Bucky Barnes
5. Janet van Dyne
6. Clint Barton

7. Peggy Carter
8. Drax the Destroyer

Puzzle 26
NAME THAT COMIC
1. *The Amazing Spider-Man*
2. *Fantastic Four*
3. *The Incredible Hulk*
4. *X-Men*
5. *The Infinity War*
6. *The Infinity Gauntlet*
7. *Silver Surfer*
8. *Squirrel Girl*
9. *Doctor Strange*
10. *The Savage She-Hulk*

Puzzle 27
WHO AM I?
Groot

Puzzle 28
MATCH THE WEAPON
Thor (Hammer)
Gorr the God Butcher
  (All-Black the Necrosword)
Captain America (Shield)
Yondu (Yaka Arrows)
Star-Lord (Element Gun)
Loki (Scepter)
Shuri (Vibranium Strike
  Gauntlets)
Thanos (Infinity Gauntlet)
Spider-Man (Web shooters)

Puzzle 29
SPOT THE DIFFERENCE

Puzzle 30
WORDSEARCH

Puzzle 31
WHO'S WHO VILLAINS?
1–H, 2–D, 3–C, 4–K, 5–F,
6–I, 7–E, 8–G, 9–B, 10–J
Ultron is the odd one out.

Puzzle 32
CODEWORD
WANDA MAXIMOFF

L	Y	S	I	N	E		L	I	Z	A	R	D
O		Q		A		I		N		K		A
C	O	U	N	T		R		D	R	I	E	R
K		I		A	M	O	U	R		H		C
J	A	B		S		N		A	M	I	T	Y
A				H		P				R		
W	A	N	D	A	M	A	X	I	M	O	F	F
		O				T		R				A
O	T	H	E	R		R		O		L	A	N
U		V		O	N	I	O	N		A		D
T	W	A	N	G		O		M	I	X	E	R
G		R		U		T		A		E		A
O	B	R	I	E	N		A	N	T	R	A	L

1 R	2 W	3 V	4 U	5 Q	6 G	7 N	8 I	9 D	10 S	11 Y	12 J	13 H
14 T	15 X	16 B	17 A	18 O	19 Z	20 L	21 M	22 F	23 C	24 E	25 K	26 P

Puzzle 33
MISSING VOWELS
1. America Chavez
2. Black Widow
3. Gamora
4. Jane Foster
5. Ms. Marvel
6. Janet Van Dyne

Puzzle 34
MULTIPLE CHOICE QUIZ
1–C, 2–A, 3–C, 4–D, 5–D, 6–B

Puzzle 35
SPATIAL AWARENESS
Only 1 is possible.

Puzzle 36
PLACE A NUMBER

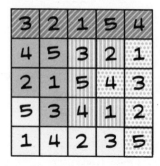

3	2	1	5	4
4	5	3	2	1
2	1	5	4	3
5	3	4	1	2
1	4	2	3	5

Puzzle 37
BREAKOUT

Puzzle 38
YNBW QUIZ
1. Black
2. Yes
3. No
4. White
5. White
6. Yes
7. Black

Puzzle 39
ODD ONE OUT
Line 1 is the odd one out. It is the only line where Wasp is not next to Ant-Man.

Puzzle 40
IN THE SHADOWS
A is the correct shadow.

Puzzle 41
BRAIN TRAINING

							6
						4	3
					9	2	1
				8	5	8	4
			5	9	2	6	7
		7	8	4	1	3	9
	2	1	6	3	8	7	5
3	8	9	7	5	4	1	2
1	7	5	8	4	2	3	9

Puzzle 42
SHIELD WORDS
GHOST
GROOT
SHURI
YONDU
BUCKY

Puzzle 43
SPOT THE DIFFERENCE

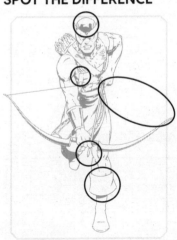

Puzzle 44
CLUED UP
1. Peter Quill/Star-Lord
2. Captain Marvel
3. Nakia
4. The Thing
5. Nebula
6. Nick Fury
7. Korg
8. Thanos

Puzzle 45
WHERE... IN THE UNIVERSE?
1. EGO
2. ASGARD
3. SKRULLOS
4. SAKAAR
5. HALA
6. XANDAR
7. TITAN
8. INDIGARR

Puzzle 46
THOR AND FRIENDS
HULK
FANDRAL
HOGUN
VOLSTAGG
JANE FOSTER

Puzzle 47
WORDSEARCH

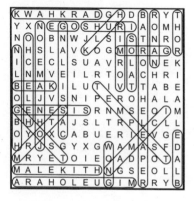

Puzzle 48
PYRAMID POWER

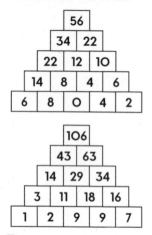

Puzzle 49
ODD ONE OUT
Line 4 is the odd one out, because it is the only one that contains three different faces; all other lines have at least two the same.

Puzzle 50
CODEWORD
ELIJAH BRADLEY

Puzzle 51
WORDSEARCH

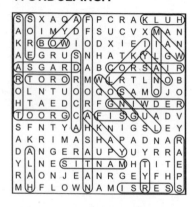

Puzzle 52
COMPLETE THE COMICS
1. *Sabretooth*
2. *Ghost Rider*
3. *Starfox*
4. *Edge of Spider-Verse*
5. *Miracleman*
6. *The Mighty Thor: Avengers Assemble*
7. *Captain America Reborn*
8. *Immortal Hulk*
9. *The Dark Phoenix Saga*
10. *The Kree-Skrull War*
11. *X-Men: Days of Future Past*
12. *Wolverine: Old Man Logan*
13. *Loki: Agent of Asgard*
14. *Savage She-Hulk*
15. *Hawkeye: Kate Bishop*

Puzzle 53
ESCAPE THE RAFT

Puzzle 54
SHIELD WORDS
STARK
OKOYE
TALOS
KURSE
MORDO

Puzzle 55
ODD IRON MAN OUT
The odd one out is on page 93, column 10, line 12.

Puzzle 56
STONE PLACEMENT

		1	
●		●	2
2	4	●	
●	2		

Puzzle 57
COMMUNICATION
HULK
LOKI
JANE
THOR
NOVA

Puzzle 58
CODEWORD
JIMMY HUDSON

Puzzle 59
SYMBOL SWEEP

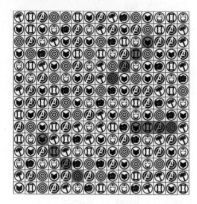

Puzzle 60
PLACE A NUMBER

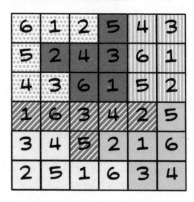

Puzzle 61
MISSING VOWELS
1. Malekith
2. Dormammu
3. Yon-Rogg
4. Kaecilius
5. Vulture
6. Mr Fantastic

Puzzle 62
IN THE SHADOWS
C is the correct shadow.

Puzzle 63
MATCHMAKER
1–B, 2–E, 3–A, 4–F, 5–J,
6–I, 7–D, 8–H, 9–G, 10–C

Puzzle 64
ASSEMBLE!

Silver Surfer
Human Torch
Squirrel Girl
Thunderbolt Ross
Invisible Woman
Flash Thompson
Black Cat
Iron Patriot

Puzzle 65
MEMORY MASTER

&	#	/	&
#	%	&	%
&	%	#	#
/	&	#	&

Puzzle 66
PYRAMID POWER

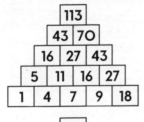

		113		
	43	70		
	16	27	43	
5	11	16	27	
1	4	7	9	18

		125		
	61	64		
	32	29	35	
19	13	16	19	
12	7	6	10	9

Puzzle 67
XAVIER'S RIDDLE

To solve the riddle put 1 book in the small box, 1 in the medium box and 2 in the large box. Then place the small box in the medium box, and both of those into the large box. That way the large box contains 4 books, the medium box contains 2 books and the small box contains 1 book. The instructions are followed by having 1, 2 and 4 books in the boxes.

Puzzle 68
ENTRY CODE

2	+	6	−	5	=	3
+		−		−		
4	+	3	+	1	=	8
+		+		+		
9	−	7	+	8	=	10
=		=		=		
15		10		12		

Puzzle 69
TRUE OR FALSE?
1. False, they have had many punch-ups.
2. True
3. True
4. False
5. True
6. False, they are made of Adamantium.
7. True
8. False, it is Stephen.

Puzzle 70
CODEWORD
CHARLES XAVIER

Puzzle 71
INCOGNITO!
1. Captain Marvel
2. Human Torch
3. Thunderbolt Ross
4. Spider-Woman
5. Invisible Woman
6. Flash Thompson
7. Miles Morales
8. Howard the Duck
9. Phil Coulson
10. Nick Fury

Puzzle 72
MULTIPLE CHOICE
1–D, 2–B, 3–B, 4–C, 5–C, 6–A

Puzzle 73
WORDSEARCH

Puzzle 74
SPOT THE DIFFERENCE

Puzzle 75
WHO AM I?
GAMORA

Puzzle 76
HIDDEN VILLAINS
1. Killmonger
2. Dormammu
3. Ultron
4. Proxima Midnight
5. Thanos
6. Malekith
7. Doctor Doom
8. Ulysses Klaw
9. Winter Soldier
10. Ebony Maw
11. Corvus Glaive
12. Whiplash

Puzzle 77
WHAT'S MY NAME?
1. Arnim Zola
2. Whiplash
3. Taserface
4. Nick Fury
5. Crossbones
6. Maria Hill
7. Star-Lord
8. Nova Prime
9. Sam Wilson
10. Spider-Man

Puzzle 78
TRUE OR FALSE?
1. False
2. True
3. True
4. True
5. True
6. False, he is a dark elf.
7. True
8. True

Puzzle 79
MINESWEEP

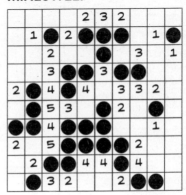

Puzzle 80
MISSING VOWELS
1. VISION
2. CAROL DANVERS
3. SHANG-CHI
4. MILES MORALES
5. GALACTUS
6. HAWKEYE

Puzzle 81
SPOT THE DIFFERENCE

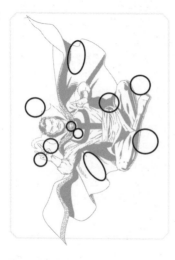

Puzzle 82
SHIELD WORDS
THANOS
GAMORA
NEBULA
ULTRON
FRIGGA
MANTIS

Puzzle 83
CODEWORD
HOWARD THE DUCK

C	R	A	G	G	Y		F	I	E	R	C	E
H		D		U		E		M		A		J
E	Q	U	I	N	O	X		B	O	M	B	E
E		L		G		C		U		B		C
T	I	T	A	N		E	V	E	R	E	T	T
A				I		P				A		
H	O	W	A	R	D	T	H	E	D	U	C	K
		R			I		N					A
A	K	I	H	I	R	O		D	R	A	W	L
Z		G		N		N		G		M		L
T	A	L	O	S		A	V	A	D	A	R	A
E		E		E		L		M		Z		R
C	O	Y	O	T	E		B	E	D	E	C	K

| 1 U | 2 K | 3 N | 4 E | 5 T | 6 O | 7 Q | 8 A | 9 C | 10 S | 11 H | 12 X | 13 J |
| 14 G | 15 Z | 16 W | 17 F | 18 I | 19 B | 20 V | 21 P | 22 D | 23 Y | 24 M | 25 R | 26 L |

Puzzle 84
MEMORY MASTER

%	#	%	>	%
>	/	%	/	?
%	/	>	%	#
>	#	>	#	%
?	>	#	?	/

Puzzle 85
PLACE A NUMBER

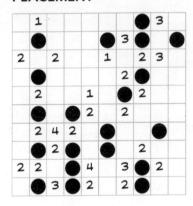

4	2	1	3	5	6
3	5	2	6	4	1
6	4	5	1	3	2
1	3	6	4	2	5
5	6	3	2	1	4
2	1	4	5	6	3

Puzzle 86
PASSWORD PLEASE
The password is Angela.

Puzzle 87
PLACEMENT

Puzzle 88
MARVEL ACROSTIC
Peter Parker
Iron Man
Doctor Strange
Emma Frost
Rogue
Magneto
Ant-Man
Nick Fury

Puzzle 89
WHO AM I?
Rocket

Puzzle 90
FLYING SOLO
Daredevil

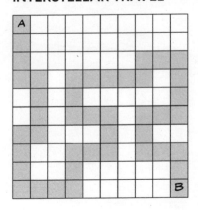

Puzzle 91
INTERSTELLAR TRAVEL

Puzzle 92
ANT-WORK

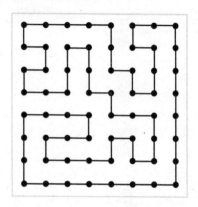

Puzzle 93
VISION'S CHALLENGE
Groups 3 and 5.

Puzzle 94
SPOT THE DIFFERENCE

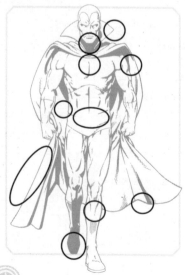

Puzzle 95
QUOTE QUIZ
"It's clobberin' time!"
  The Thing
"By the hoary hosts of
  Hoggoth!"
Doctor Strange
"To me, my board!"
  The Silver Surfer
"My Spider-sense is tingling!"
  Spider-Man
"Flame on!"
  The Human Torch
"By Odin's Beard!" Thor
"Imperius rex!" Namor

Puzzle 96
NAME THAT CHARACTER
1. Rocket Racer
2. Speedball
3. Squirrel Girl
4. Hobgoblin
5. Mr Fantastic
6. Jean Grey/Phoenix
7. Ms. Marvel
8. Nova
9. Storm
10. America Chavez

Puzzle 97
TIMED ANALYSIS
Squares C and D.

Puzzle 98
MACRO VISION
4 and 7 are identical.

Puzzle 99
SUM IT UP

23	+	18	×	21	−	9	+	19	=	411
−		×		−		+		×		
8	÷	4	−	20	+	6	×	5	=	12
+		+		+		+		−		
11	÷	22	×	16	−	10	−	14	=	-16
+		−		−		+		+		
13	+	1	+	3	+	25	+	24	=	66
+		+		−		−		÷		
17	−	15	×	7	−	12	÷	2	=	-94
=		=		=		=		=		
56		108		7		38		93		

Puzzle 100
PLACE A NUMBER

2	6	7	5	1	3	4
5	1	4	3	7	6	2
7	3	2	6	4	1	5
6	2	1	4	3	5	7
1	5	3	7	2	4	6
3	4	5	2	6	7	1
4	7	6	1	5	2	3

183